MIG-29 prototype, "9-01", currently is on display at the Soviet Air Force Museum at Monino, just outside Moscow. This aircraft differed considerably from the standard production configuration particularly in nose radome design, the application of ventral fins, and nose landing gear placement. Visible in the background is the prototype MiG-23.

CREDITS:

The author and Aerofax, Inc. would like to thank the following individuals for assistance provided in the completion of this book: Anatoly Belosvet, Miriam Ben-Shalom, Michael Binder, Seffy Bodansky, Piotr Butowski, Dick Cole, Tom Copeland, Greg Fieser, Charles Fleming, Kelly Green, Goran Henriksson, Dennis Jenkins, Kalevi Keskinen, Tony Landis, Andrzej Lesicki, Valery Menitsky, Eddie Moore, Scott Newman, Klaus Niska, Dick Pawloski, Chris Pocock, Tom Ring, Albert Ross, Mick Roth, Robert Ruffle, Eva Smoke, Kari Stenman, Sven Stridsberg, John W. R. Taylor, Katsuhiko Tokunaga, Frans Uytenhout, Theodore Van Geffen, Alexander Velovitch, Barbara Wasson, Rainer Wiceen, and Bryan Wilburn.

PROGRAM HISTORY:

The death of Artyom Mikoyan on December 9, 1970, following open heart surgery, signaled the beginning of the end for the old guard in the Mikoyan and Gurevich (MIG) experimental design bureau (OKB/*Opytno konstruktorskoe byuro*). Though co-founder Mikhail Gurevich still was living, he no longer participated in the OKB's day-to-day activities and most of the designers on hand had started working at the bureau long after he and Mikoyan had opened its doors for the first time during 1939. Mikoyan's deputy, Rostislav Belyakov, one of the last active old guard personalities, now took control of the bureau's operation (he had, in fact, been in control in an unofficial capacity since 1968) and during 1971 was declared chief engineer. As such, Belyakov became the most powerful person in the bureau's hierarchy.

When Mikoyan died, he took with him a sizable chunk of bureau history. As one of the grand old men of Soviet aviation, he had been greatly respected by his many national and international colleagues, and his accomplishments and list of titles and honors was extraordinary.

During 1971, the OKB formally was renamed after Artyom Mikoyan—with Gurevich's name being removed temporarily from the MIG acronym. Belyakov, however, had not forgotten Mikoyan's words during Gurevich's 1964 formal retirement ceremony wherein he stated, "Even though Mikhail leaves the team, our aircraft are, and forever will be named MIG". Belyakov elected to honor this declaration and accordingly, to this very day, all aircraft produced by what technically is the Belyakov OKB continue to be delivered bearing the proud MIG acronym.[1]

Rostislav Apollosovich Belyakov had become a member of the Mikoyan team during 1941 following graduation from the Moscow Aviation Institute (MAI). Even with the *Great Patriotic War* making virtually everything difficult, he managed to complete his required apprenticeship and to work as part of the team undertaking the modernization of the MIG-1 and MIG-3 series fighter armament systems. His area of specialization at the time was

---

[1] Interestingly, it should be noted that during 1990 the bureau made a decision to spell MIG with all capital letters. The reason for this remains unclear as of this writing, but the many-decades-old-convention of spelling MiG with a small "i" now is history.

MIG-29A, "49", was one of approximately 100 initial production series "Fulcrums" built with ventral fins. These later were removed with no adverse affect on directional stability at high angles of attack.

1

Gordon Swanborough collection

MIG-29 production facility at GAZ-30, just outside Moscow. Though a reasonably high-technology aircraft, production techniques utilized to build it are generally antiquated and highly labor-intensive.

Gordon Swanborough collection

Many MIG-29 parts are hand-formed and hand-fitted, thus making parts interchangeability in the field a difficult proposition. Visible in this view is IRST dome assembly and radar mounting unit.

Aerofax, Inc. collection

What appears to be a full-scale MIG-29A mock-up undergoing wind tunnel testing under the aegis of the TsAGI. This is a late-model "Fulcrum". Noteworthy are extended flap trailing edges and fixed exhaust nozzles.

aerodynamics, but the exigencies of war forced him to learn other aircraft technologies as well. Accordingly, he became involved in the design of landing gear, control systems, and eventually, the initial total design phases of the MIG-1, MIG-3 and several later MIG products.

A year after joining the MIG bureau Belyakov became a deputy chief designer and eventually was made manager of landing gear systems for the post-war MIG jets. In concert with this responsibility he developed a considerable expertise in hydraulic systems and later was totally responsible for integrating them into the landing gear, flaps, and airbrakes of the highly successful MIG-15.

Belyakov later became the bureau's chief authority on hydraulically-boosted flight control systems and still later played a key role in the development of slab-type horizontal tail surfaces and their associated hydraulic actuators. This latter effort, coupled with a related development program calling for a refined system-integrated auto-pilot, eventually played a key role in the subsequent successes enjoyed by the MIG-19.

During 1955 Belyakov successfully managed the OKB's design brigade. Two years later, partially as a result of its success and his previous contributions to OKB products, he was appointed deputy engineer in charge of control systems. His efforts in the latter position eventually bore fruit in the form of the Ye-150, the Ye-152, and the MIG-25.

During 1962, Belyakov became Mikoyan's deputy and directly managed the construction and testing of many OKB aircraft including the MIG-23, MIG-25, and MIG-27. He also coordinated OKB activities with those of other research institutes, design teams, and the various industrial plants, and consequently served as a liaison between the OKB and government engineers, pilots, and military units that were directly involved with MIG aircraft operations. During this period he was given the title of Hero of Socialist Work and was presented with the prestigious Lenin Award. A year after Mikoyan's death, he was made OKB General Engineer and invited to become a member of the Soviet Academy of Sciences. During this period, the MIG-29 and MIG-31 were created under his direction and he was a delegate to the Convention of the Communist Party of the Soviet Union.

Perhaps the most significant of the many MIG aircraft with which Belyakov has been involved is the MIG-29. Developed in response to lessons learned by both the US and the Soviet Union during air combat over Vietnam and other areas of conflict during the 1960s and 1970s, it is today representative of state-of-the-art fighter design in the Soviet Union and considered one of the most effective air combat aircraft in the world.

The MIG-29 first was conceived as a study during the mid-1970s when the VVS (Soviet Air Force) and associated aviation research institutes began to notice a trend in US fighter design calling for improved maneuverability. In essence, what had been learned by the US during air combat in Vietnam skies was that the "beyond visual range" (BVR) radar-guided air-to-air missile philosophy so highly regarded during the 1950s, was not a viable concept during the 1960s—and that the long-standing trend away from maneuverable fighters and visual contact with the enemy was a nearly catastrophic mistake.

Because of this generic analysis, a new philosophy emerged calling for the development of more maneuverable platforms that retained a modicum of BVR capability, but placed more emphasis on "dog-fighting" and working one-on-one with a target. Resulting from this came a variety of new fighters, including the Grumman F-14, the McDonnell Douglas F-15, the General Dynamics

F-16, and the McDonnell Douglas F/A-18. All of these aircraft, with the possible exception of the F-14, were heavily compromised in favor of maneuverability, and with the F-16 in particular, the general bias of the airframe all but discarded the BVR option.

As these US programs began to surface, Soviet technical intelligence teams gathered available data wherever possible and ran the synthesized information across to the various design bureaus for analysis. As a result, the maneuverability trend was noted and studied, and the inadequacies of then-state-of-the-art Soviet fighters were reviewed.

The general consensus of opinion among the various Soviet research institutes, government bureaucracies, and design bureaus was that extant Soviet combat aircraft were not going to be competitive during the late 1970s and early 1980s and that no short term solution was in sight. Only a commitment to a new generation of fighters to offset the forthcoming lack of parity could hope to counter the emerging performance inequities.

By the early 1970s, studies had been initiated at the various bureaus with the objective of developing a family of fighters that could compete with the new US aircraft. Sukhoi and MIG, because of their normal fighter orientation, became the prime contenders in this retrenchment, and by the middle of the decade had begun to solidify designs and build prototype hardware based on input from the TsAGI (*Tsentral'ny aerogidrodinamicheski institut*/Central Aero and Hydrodynamics Institute). The latter had, by this time, evolved a number of potential solutions to the problems presented by the projected performance envelope and as a result, both bureaus worked with designs that utilized twin vertical tail surfaces, ramp-type rectangular format intakes mounted under wing root section chines, and raised cockpits with virtually 360° visibility.

As it were, Sukhoi, initially under the leadership of Evgeniy Ivanov and later under the leadership of Mikhail Simonov, had been tasked with the design and development of a large, long-range fighter comparable in many respects to the McDonnell Douglas F-15 and later identified as the Su-27; and MIG, under the leadership of Rostislav Belyakov and his deputy, Mikhail Waldenberg, had been

Katsuhiko Tokunaga

A fully-armed MIG-29A was displayed for the first time during the 1990 Farnborough Airshow in England. The aircraft's weapons compliment included the rarely seen vectorable-thrust R-73 air-to-air missile.

Aerofax, Inc. collection

Views of the MIG-29 in flight in clean configuration are rare, due to the aircraft's limited range without external fuel tanks. Range remains the "Fulcrum's" major failing in the combat role.

Aerofax, Inc. collection

A rare photo of an operational early-model MIG-29A. Readily visible in this view are the ventral fins peculiar to the initial production aircraft. Also discernible is the outline of a centerline drop tank. This aircraft also has the original vertical fin leading edge extensions without chaff/flare dispensers.

An extremely clean MIG-29A, ''06'', was placed on static display at Kubinka AB during an August of 1988 exchange visit with the USAF. A sister aircraft, ''05'', provided the first public domain cockpit photos.

Operational VVS MIG-29s now have participated in a number of exchange visits. The first of these, comprising six single-seat aircraft, took place at Rissala AB, Finland, during July of 1986.

tasked with the design and development of a considerably smaller and more maneuverable fighter eventually designated MIG-29 and comparable in many respects to the General Dynamics F-16.

Prior to initiation of construction of the first few prototypes, MIG moved ahead with a program of computer modeling investigations, simulator studies, and wind tunnel tests (including low-speed work in the TsAGI's T-128 tunnel) in order to verify the basic design parameters of the full-scale aircraft. Heavy emphasis was placed on studying the new fighter's vortex system and areas of maximum vortex efficiency. The latter were given special attention and exploratory work refined them in order to assure exceptional maneuverability performance.

New manufacturing processes specific to MIG-29 materials and production requirements also were under development at this time. The production line at Plant No. 30 just outside Moscow, for instance, was optimized to utilize automated welding processes as part of the tooling process,

and this equipment was installed prior to the construction of the first prototype aircraft. Additionally, the MIG-29 became one of the first MIG fighters to utilize composites and the specific materials incorporated were developed indigenously by the bureau.

By mid-1975 the design of the new fighter essentially had been established and construction of the first of what eventually would be eleven prototypes was initiated at the bureau's Leningradskiye Shassi (highway) facility. On October 6, 1977, the first MIG-29 prototype, with the call numbers ''9-01'' painted on its nose and bureau chief test pilot Alexander Fedotov at the controls, took to the air from the Ramenskoye[2] flight test facility for the first time. Lasting just over an hour, the flight was successful and Fedotov later debriefed without difficulty in front of a relatively anxious bureau engineering team.

Eight months later, during June of 1978, the second prototype was test flown from Ramenskoye by Valery Menitsky and assigned to the RD-33 engine test program. The third prototype flew during October of 1978 and a fourth aircraft was added to the test fleet during 1979. The fifth prototype was assigned the task of testing performance and handling qualities, the sixth was used for radar development, the seventh and ninth aircraft were used for fire control systems integration, and the eighth was used for structural loads analysis. Aircraft ten and eleven were used as full-scale-development (FSD) configuration patterns with number ten serving to explore aerodynamic and engine requirements and number eleven serving the needs of the fire control system integration team.

Initial testing of the MIG-29 lasted approximately eight months and was accommodated by Fedotov and Menitsky. With the addition of the third and following prototypes, other bureau test pilots entered the program including Pyotr Ostapenko, Boris Orlov, and Aviard Fastovets. Still later, Toktar Aubakirov, Anatoly Kvochur, Viktor Ryndin, and Roman Taskayev also became part of the bureau's MIG-29 flight test team. Menitsky later would become MIG's chief test pilot following Fedotov's death in a MIG-31 accident on April 4, 1984. Once VVS involvement became mandatory, military pilots including Migunov, Kontraourov, Gorbunov, Lotkov, and Khraptsov joined the effort.

The MIG-29 flight test program, conducted not only at Ramenskoye but also at facilities on the Volga, the Crimean peninsula, and several other sites, did not go smoothly at first. Difficulties, including compressor stalls and catastrophic failures of the RD-33 turbofan engine led to several accidents. The No. 2 aircraft was lost after the failure of an engine mounting latch caused an uncontrollable inflight titanium casing fire, and the No. 4 aircraft was lost following an engine combustion chamber explosion. Menitsky was piloting No. 2 and Fedotov was piloting No. 4 at the time of their respective losses. Both pilots suffered serious injuries, but recovered to fly again.[3]

The MIG-29 flight test program was divided into three stages. The first was referred to as ''Plant Flight Testing'' and was carried out only by bureau pilots. The second stage was called ''Design Flight Testing'' and served primarily to expose military

All six of the MIG-29As sent to Rissala are seen during a fly past upon their July 1986 exchange visit arrival. Moments later they had broken formation for landing.

[2] The Ramenskoye flight test facility now is more commonly referred to as the Zhukovksy flight test facility in the Soviet Union. This is due to the local habit of naming airfields after the nearest large town. Originally, Ramenskoye was the largest town near the base. Near-by Zhukovsky, however, since has undergone a considerable population explosion and as a result now is larger than Ramenskoye, thus leading to the name change. Because of its greater familiarity to westerners, however, the name Ramenskoye will be used in this book.

[3] Several other serious accidents occurred during the course of the later high-angle-of-attack and spin test programs, but details are lacking.

MIG-29A "12" taxiing out for takeoff. Visible in this view are the closed FOD doors in the intake tunnels. These do no open until aircraft weight comes off the main landing gear struts. In the interim, intake air is provided via louvered intake slots with spring-loaded doors on the fuselage chine surfaces above the intake tunnels.

pilots to the aircraft for the first time. And the third stage was called "State Flight Testing" and served to allow military pilots to fully exploit the aircraft in a pre-operational setting while certifying it for use by the VVS.

In the west, information concerning the new MIG fighter—then tentatively identified as *RAM-L* (in consideration of its appearance at Ramenskoye during reconnaissance satellite observation of this well-known test base)—began to surface outside intelligence bureaus during 1979. By mid-1982, following a change in the nose landing gear position (production aircraft, flight tested after completion at near-by Lukhovitsy field, had nose gear struts approximately 1 ft. [.31 m.] further aft than the prototypes), deletion of the twin ventral fins (the surface area was increased on the vertical fin root extensions to compensate for this; there is some indication that the first 100 or so production aircraft were equipped with ventral fins but these later were removed), and the repositioning of various antennas and pressure sensors, the MIG-29 had gone into full-scale production at the *Znamya Truda*[4] factory near Moscow. By the following year, it was beginning to equip indigenous Soviet fighter squadrons in ever-increasing numbers.

The initial single-seat MIG-29 later formally was identified in the west as the MIG-29A and codenamed *Fulcrum-A* by NATO. There have been, in fact, some minor upgrades to this first derivative, these being distinguishable primarily in the form of extended rudder chords (past the vertical tail trailing edge) and other minor changes. A further improved variant, which some sources claim has been designated MIG-29M, currently is undergoing flight test, but little information is available as of this writing. However, this aircraft

[4] Located on Moscow's Bokhtinskaya street, this is the oldest aircraft factory in the Soviet Union. It first was utilized for aircraft construction during 1909 while still the *Dux* bicycle shop. Nikolai Lenin's glass-covered casket was built here following his death during 1924, and during 1939, as aircraft factory No.1, it served as the first office for the fledgling MIG OKB. Today this massive facility is named *Znamya Truda* ("The Banner of Labor") and is under the direction of A. Manuyev. It presently employs approximately 30,000 people (with some 3,000 of these producing consumer goods), covers some 617 acres (250 hectares) of land, and contains 26,909,675 ft.^{2} (2,500,000 m.^{2}) of floor space.

may be the experimental fly-by-wire-equipped[5] aircraft that also features a four cathode-ray-tube main instrument panel display similar to that found on the McDonnell Douglas F/A-18. This aircraft has been referred to as an "intermediate MIG-29" by General Designer Rostislav Belyakov and is acknowledged still to be in flight test. If it eventually enters production, it may become the first operational Soviet fighter to be equipped with a side-stick controller.

Additionally, as part of a program initiated during 1985, at least one MIG-29A, as the MIG-29K, was modified for carrier trials and equipped with strengthened landing gear, folding wings, a tailhook, a thermal imaging sensor ball in place of the standard infrared sensor, and miscellaneous other carrier-compatible systems and upgrades

[5] The MIG-29's experimental fly-by-wire system apparently was at least partly the responsibility of MIG OKB deputy chief designer Anatoly Belosvet.

(importantly, the hydraulically-actuated intake doors and associated dorsally-mounted auxiliary intakes and their spring-loaded doors have been removed). Actual carrier trials aboard the 60,000-plus ton Soviet aircraft carrier *Tbilisi* began on November 1, 1989 and approximately 20 landings and takeoffs were completed. MIG bureau deputy chief test pilot Taktar Aubakirov flew the aircraft. An approach speed of 149 mph (240 km/h) was used and the average a-o-a was approximately 13° to 14°. The trials later were deemed completely successful and there now appears to be a very good chance for a navalized MIG-29 to enter production.

Little information, as of this writing, has been leaked to the west concerning future MIG-29 developments, but the following items are planned and almost certainly will start appearing on testbed and operational aircraft during the mid-1990s: improved radar and avionics systems; digital electronic engine controls (though present

MIG-29s also were involved in an exchange visit with the Finnish Air Force during July of 1989. Rissala AB again was the site of the event, with the VVS aircraft parked statically across from Finnish MIG-21bises.

Dick Pavloski collection

Piloted by a Col. Viktor Bytskov, MIG-29A, "02", lost its brake chute shortly after touching down during an exchange visit demonstration at Rissala AB, Finland on February 19, 1989. Following the failure, the aircraft entered the overrun barrier at a speed of approximately 10 kts. Only minor damage was incurred.

Sven Stridsberg

The July 1989 exchange visit by VVS MIG-29As at Rissala AB near Kuopio was done not only with the intent of generating good will, but also with the intent of selling the excellent Soviet fighter to the Finnish Air Force. The latter, long a user of Soviet combat aircraft, rejected the "Fulcrum" during 1990 and continues to explore alternative aircraft.

DoD

Single canopy drag chute on the MIG-29A is stored in a canister mounted in the extreme aft end of the abbreviated fuselage empennage section. Just in front of, and above and below the canister is a split, hydraulically-actuated airbrake assembly that can be used both in flight and during roll-out. FOD-doors function as weight is placed on main gear.

hydromechanical systems will be retained as a back-up); horizontal tail modifications; repositioned wing for improved relaxed static stability (to take better advantage of the fly-by-wire systems that will be integrated); and updated cockpit controls and displays. The Navy-optimized variant also will incorporate the following changes: no auxiliary engine inlets and FOD doors; structural upgrades to the fuselage and landing gear; a tailhook; tube launched missile capability; and inflight refueling. Additionally, the Navy aircraft may incorporate canard surfaces on the forward fuselage. Finally, there will likely be a dedicated ground-attack derivative.

To complement the single-seat MIG-29A and the newer upgraded NATO *Fulcrum-C* (nicknamed *Fatback*, this version is equipped with an enlarged dorsal hump providing increased internal volume for fuel and electronics), the MIG-29UB also has been built. This variant, with two ejection seats mounted in tandem under an extended canopy, is a dedicated trainer and thus not pulse-Doppler radar equipped. It does have a small range-finding radar in the nose and the infrared sensor ball has been retained. Dimensions have generally been only slightly affected, with over-all length being increased by some 3.9 in. (10 cm.) over the single-seat aircraft. Combat capability remains extremely limited.

Between July 1 and July 4, 1986, a group of six MIG-29As undertook an exchange visit to Rissala air base near Kuopio in Finland. This was a continuation of an on-going cooperative exchange program between Kuopio and Kubin near Moscow that first had been undertaken during 1974. Every four years since, Soviet pilots have exchanged visits with their Finnish counterparts, and usually, these have provided western observers an opportunity to view the newest in Soviet fighter technology, first-hand. During 1974, for instance, the MIG-21bis was presented, and a visit later, the MIG-23L turned up.

On the second day of the 1986 visit, the MIG-29As were demonstrated in the air. Vladimir Chilin was the first to become airborne and immediately began a solo routine that proved decidedly impressive; following a 1,604 ft. (500 m.) takeoff run, he immediately began his performance by entering a dynamic vertical climb. Once at altitude, he then entered the first of a lengthy repertoire of aerobatic maneuvers, after which he landed. Roll-out following touch-down was only 1,444 ft. (450 m.). A group of four MIG-29As took off shortly after his landing, providing a demonstration of the aircraft's formation aerobatic capabilities.

The MIG-29, during the 1988 Farnborough Airshow, became the first high-performance Soviet fighter ever to be displayed there. Two aircraft, a MIG-29A and a MIG-29UB, following a formal announcement of their coming on July 17, 1988, flew to England via Wittstock in East Germany. Over the British Isles they were welcomed by two RAF BAC *Tornado F3s* and a single Vickers VC-10. The MIG-29A was piloted by Anatoly Kvotchur and the MIG-29UB was piloted by Roman Taskayev with Yuriy Yermakov in the back seat. Chief designer Rostislav Belyakov, deputy chief designer Mikhail Waldenberg, and chief test pilot Valery Menitsky later appeared at the static display.

During the Farnborough show, the MIG-29 performed daily. The routine included a slow speed pass at approximately 124 mph (200 km/h) and an angle-of-attack of about 25° (MIG bureau personnel claim the maximum a-o-a is 30° at this airspeed). A 360° turn was accomplished in 12.5 to 16 secs. on average and a maximum sustained g-load of 9 was demonstrated. Additionally, a 2,246 ft. (700 m.) dia. turn was accomplished at

During 1989 Rissala AB exchange visit, MIG-29A "02" landed too fast and too high. The drag chute failed shortly after deployment and the aircraft was forced to utilize the runway crash barrier. Damage was slight.

MIG-29A "12" was the solo routine aircraft during the 1986 Rissala AB exchange visit. Noteworthy in this view is the retraction sequence of the landing gear at mid-point. Antonov An-12 is visible below.

MIG-29A's arrival at the 1989 Paris Airshow permitted the first detailed look at the aircraft external fuel tank option. Visible on intake cheek to left is MIG bureau logo.

Aerofax, Inc. collection

Though optimized in design for air superiority, the MIG-29 apparently has proven very capable as a ground support aircraft. Rocket pods are visible suspended from the four inboard pylons.

Alex Porteous via John Taylor

The "Fulcrum" was introduced to the west formally during the 1988 Farnborough Airshow in England. Both a single-seat MIG-29A and a two-seat MIG-29UB accompanied the Mikoyan bureau contingent.

a speed of 497 mph (800 km/h). A smaller turn of some 1,444 ft. (450 m.) in dia., flown at 3.8 gs also was accomplished at a speed of approximately 248 mph (400 km/h). Level flight acceleration was clocked at approximately 35 ft./sec. (11 m./sec.) at sea level at Mach 0.85. It later was estimated that it would take 13 secs. for the MIG-29 to accelerate from 311 to 621 mph (500 to 1,000 km/h) at sea level. At 19,250 ft. (6,000 m.) and Mach 0.85, acceleration was estimated to be 21 ft./sec. (6.5 m./sec.).

One of the more visually stunning elements of the MIG-29's Farnborough performance was its demonstrated ability to do tail-slides at low altitudes. The maneuver, in which the aircraft initially climbed vertically and slowly decelerated to the point where it stopped and then descended still with its nose pointing vertically, is considered not particularly dangerous at altitude, but is precarious because of the potential for engine flame-out. Kvotchur's particular maneuver was impressive because as it was performed regularly at an altitude no higher than 2,887 ft. to 3,208 ft. (900 m. to 1,000 m.)—which almost certainly was too low for recovery in the event of engine failure.

Perhaps Kvotchur's most spectacular performance occurred just over half a year after his Farnborough debut. On June 8, 1989, while flying a MIG-29A at the 38th Aeronautical Salon at Le Bourget (better known simply as the Paris Airshow), a starboard engine failure forced him to eject while the aircraft was flying at 112 mph (180

km/h) at about 513 ft. (160 m.). As he ejected, the aircraft began a roll toward its starboard side and then decended in an almost perfect vertical attitude. No more than 1.5 seconds after Kvotchur egressed, the aircraft hit the ground and was totally destroyed. In the interim, Kvotchur's parachute opened fully—literally at the moment his feet touched the earth's surface. The K-36DM ejection seat unquestionably had saved his life. Kvotchur received only minor injuries.

The MIG-29 has become successful not only in VVS service, but in the air forces of several foreign contries, as well. Through January of 1991, the MIG bureau claims to have sold a total of 250 MIG-29s to a variety of foreign customers, including the following:

Afghanistan—Sale of the MIG-29 to Afghanistan is said to have taken place during September of 1989. No additional information has surfaced.

Algeria—Sale of the MIG-29A and MIG-29UB to the Algerian Air Force was expected to be consummated during 1990.

Cuba—An unknown number of MIG-29As and MIG-29UBs are reported to have been delivered to the Cuban government during late 1989.

Czechoslovakia—Though some aircraft had been delivered during 1989, Czechoslovakian Defence Minister Miroslav Vacek stated during January of 1990 that his government had abandoned further purchases of the MIG-29A and MIG-29UB. He did not enlarge on the numbers already received but added that aircraft already

acquired would be utilized to supplement the MIG-21 in the air-defence role.

East Germany—The East German Air Force became the first Warsaw Pact country to receive the MIG-29 when the initial group of aircraft (eventually totaling at 28 MIG-29As and 4 MIG-29UBs and purportedly costing some $640 million) arrived during May of 1988. These aircraft were assigned to the Vladmir Kamarov fighter wing based in Preschen. At the end of 1990, during the formal transition of East and West Germany into a single unified Germany under western political control, the status of the East German MIG-29 fleet had yet to be determined. In the interim, select East German MIG-29s have been utilized in a detailed study program to determine its effectiveness in the air combat role. Various western aircraft, including McDonnell Douglas F-15Cs and Panavia *Tornado* GR.1s have flown against it in mock combat. These tests, during December of 1990 followed a series of evaluation flights conducted during November by the Luftwaffe's *Erprobungsstelle* 61 test and evaluation unit.

Finland—Acquisition of ex-East German Air Force MIG-29As and MIG-29UBs was considered by the Finnish Air Force during 1990 but was rejected during November of that year. A precondition as part of the deal was that the Soviet Union effectively off-set 100% of the cost of the aircraft by buying from Finland commodities with an equivalent value. This did not prove possible in light of the Soviet economic situation and Finland removed the MIG-29 from its list of contenders (the others being the General Dynamics F-16, the Dassault *Mirage* 2000, and the Saab JAS39 *Gripen*).

Hungary—The Hungarian Air Force received an undisclosed number of MIG-29As and MIG-29UBs during 1989.

India—Some 40 MIG-29As and 4 MIG-29UBs have been delivered at a "privileged purchaser" price of $11 million each. The MIG-29 is referred to as the *Baaz* (Eagle) in Indian Air Force service. Additional aircraft are expected to be built from indigenously-manufactured parts by Hindustan Aeronautics (India) at its Nasik factory. The first Indian Air Force pilots to fly the MIG-29 did so during 1984 and training of Indian Air Force personnel began during October of 1986. Introduction into service took place officially on December 6, 1987, at Poona AFB near Bombay.

Iran—During December of 1989 it was announced the Iranian government was negotiating with the Soviet Union to buy MIG-29s. It appears that an agreement was signed during June 1990. Approximately 12 MIG-29As and 2 MIG-29UBs were ordered. No further information has surfaced.

Iraq—Received some 40 MIG-29As and MIG-29UBs during 1987. These aircraft, which purportedly cost Iraq $28 million ea., presently are playing a key defensive role in the on-going Gulf crises.

Jordan—The Jordanian Air Force seriously entertained the possibility of acquiring MIG-29s in order to replace its aging fleet of Dassault *Mirage* F-1s during 1987, but is now presumed that no hardware was delivered and no deal was consummated.

Nigeria—Sale of the MIG-29A and MIG-29UB was expected to be consummated during 1990.

North Korea—Received 20 MIG-29As and MIG-29UBs during 1987.

Poland—Received first of undisclosed number of MIG-29As and MIG-29UBs during late 1989.

Romania—Has received 14 MIG-29As and 2 MIG-29UBs. Assigned to 2 *Escadrila* @ Kogalniceanu.

Switzerland—The Swiss government is stated to have expressed an interest in the acquistion of the redundant East German Air Force MIG-29s.

Syria—The Syrian Air Force has received at

least 20 MIG-29As and MIG-29UBs and along with them a significant number of *Aphid, Apex,* and possibly *Alamo* and *Archer* air-to-air missiles. Some sources indicate that the slightly demilitarized Syrian MIG-29s, first delivered during July of 1987, are referred to as MIG-30s. These aircraft are thought to have become fully operational during October or November of 1988. A three-squadron regiment now is thought to exist.

Thailand—During late 1990, the Soviet Union offered the Thai Air Force MIG-29s to complement its fleet of 24 General Dynamics F-16s. To date, no Thai commitment has been consummated.

Yugoslavia—The Yugoslavian Air Force received an initial allotment of 16 MIG-29As during October of 1987. An additional 32 aircraft were expected to follow these, though there were problems in accommodating the MIG-29s in the old MIG-21 shelters. The MIG-29 first was demonstrated publicly in Yugoslavia on May 14, 1988. In Yugoslavian Air Force service, MIG-29s are designated L-18 (Lovac/fighter).

Zimbabwe—Sale of the MIG-29A and MIG-29UB was expected to be consummated during 1990.

Miscellaneous—Though the west has been given considerable access to the MIG-29 both in the Soviet Union and at various airshows, at least one other aircraft inadvertently has been made available, at least for short term examination. On May 20, 1989, a MIG-29 was flown to Turkey by defecting pilot Alexander Zuyev. This aircraft later was returned to Tskhakaya in Soviet Georgia afterwards, but not before it was X-rayed and photographed by Turkish intelligence personnel. Turkey's prompt return of the MIG-29 to the Soviet Union proved somewhat of a controversial event at the time due to the fact that US intelligence personnel were not given access to the aircraft. Zuyev, however, moved to the US and quickly was granted political asylum.

During late 1990 it also was rumored that at least one MIG-29UB was undergoing flight testing at the USAF's secret facility at Groom Lake, Nevada. Observers claim to have seen this aircraft on several occasions sans camouflage and bearing USAF markings.

As a result of *Desert Shield* and *Desert Storm,* the MIG-29 has been utilized in actual combat for the first time in its history. The results of the various air combat skirmishes have been observed with a keen eye by all participants, as this is the first known instance wherein contemporary state-of-the-art Soviet and US combat aircraft types actually have met in combat.

Early results indicate US fighters have maintained a significant edge over their Soviet counterparts and the *status quo* of the past several decades has been maintained. On January 17, during the pre-dawn hours of *Desert Storm's* first day, at least four MIG-29s were destroyed in air-to-air combat. The *Fulcrums* had been scrambled from alert bases around Baghdad. Shortly afterwards, because of the effectiveness of Allied EW aircraft, the MIG-29s were seen to wander aimlessly, obviously without ground control assistance.

In three separate incidents, patrolling McDonnell Douglas F-15Cs from the 33rd TFW at Eglin AFB and the 1st TFW at Langley AFB achieved long range radar contact, confirmed their MIG-29 targets electronically, and fired one or two AIM-7M *Sparrows* at "no escape" ranges. In still another incident, a MIG-29 was destroyed during a low-altitude intercept of a General Dynamics F-111 when the latter off-loaded its bomb complement ahead of its attacker. The bombs exploded just in front of the *Fulcrum,* causing it to crash.

To date at least eight, and possibly as many as a dozen MIG-29s have been destroyed in combat. A number of the remaining Iraqi Air Force aircraft

MIG-29A "07" was one of the original six aircraft flown into Rissala AB during 1986. Noteworthy is flat black anti-glare panel ahead of windscreen and open lateral dorsal intake slots.

Entire undersurface of all observed "Fulcrums", including this Rissala MIG-29A, has been light grey (approx. F.S. 36375). Noteworthy is insignia position and various chine dielectric panels.

MIG-29A, "01", intercepted near Norway, was equipped with four AA-8s on its outer wing pylons and two AA-10s on its inboard wing pylons. Six pylons with various weapon options are available.

9

Martin Fricke via John Taylor

MIG-29A during 1988 Farnborough show, shortly after lift-off and immediately prior to beginning of aerobatic display. Main gear doors have yet to close and exhaust nozzles are in their maximum afterburner position. Performance of MIG-29A during course of show was first indication to west the ''Fulcrum'' was a truly effective air combat platform.

Aerolax, Inc. collection

During the summer of 1990 a special visit to Ceske Bredejovice AB in Czechoslovakia by a Guard unit of the VVS (note emblem on intake cheek) provided an extremely rare opportunity to view the most advanced operational MIG-29 variant, the ''Fulcrum C''. Nicknamed ''Fatback'', it has rarely been photographed and little is known about its capabilities.

Aerolax, Inc. collection

The MIG-29 now has appeared at airshows throughout North America and Europe—which is a first for any operational front line Soviet fighter. Because of this, major displays at the Farnborough and Paris airshows have come to be expected of the Soviets and there is word that a 1991 airshow will provide the west its first view of the new fly-by-wire MIG-29.

have taken safe haven in Iran, having escaped at low altitude across the Iran/Iraq border.

The MIG-29's combat capabilities, though somewhat clouded by security considerations, are considerably better known than many other Soviet aircraft types due in part to the aircraft's exposure at various airshows, and in part to the fact that a number of knowledgeable western pilots have been permitted flying privileges. It is, perhaps, the latter that has been the most revealing of the many opportunities to analyze the aircraft, and a synthesis of the derived information has surfaced at times in the lay press. Many details have come from these published reports, including the following tidbits:

(1) The RD-33 engines, which initially were stated by the Tumansky bureau to have a time-between-overhauls (TBO) of some 300 hours, have a true TBO of approximately 50 hours. This difficulty is being addressed and apparently, rapidly overcome.

(2) Operational surge rates (i.e., mission rates) for five days or less run an average of 4 missions per day with a decline to about 3 missions per day over a sustained 30 day period. A maximum 1 day surge rate could result in up to 6 missions.

(3) The *Fulcrum C* is thought to have an improved ground attack capability over that of earlier versions. This is a mission originally considered outside the basic capabilities of the MIG-29A. The *Fulcrum C* with its increased fuel capacity and upgraded avionics possibly has the range and loiter capability required of a truly effective ground support aircraft.

(4) Range apparently is the MIG-29's Achilles' heel; in a fully loaded condition it does not have sufficient ''legs'' to provide the area coverage normally expected of a modern fighter.

(5) The MIG-29's weapon system is not representative of western state-of-the-art and in fact is considerably more reminiscent of technology found on western aircraft of the late 1960s and early 1970s. Pilot/cockpit interfacing is poor, at best, and most of the instrumentation is analog. Many switches are difficult to access, control methodology at times is nonsensical, and overall integration is poor. On the plus side, many aspects of the cockpit are extremely practical, the cockpit is generally comfortable, vision is good (though not fully 360°—and not comparable to any state-of-the-art western fighters), and perceived capability of the aircraft over-all is excellent.

To date, approximately 750 MIG-29s have been built with approximately 500 of these in use by VVS units. The remaining 250 aircraft have been shipped to miscellaneous customers. Public domain information pertaining to future developments is slim. Other than a side comment made by Rostislav Belyakov during the 1988 Farnborough airshow wherein he stated MIG was working on fighters comparable to the American ATF and the French Dassault *Rafale,* little has surfaced in the west concerning the bureau's future plans for the MIG-29 and any follow-on aircraft.

There is little question, however, that next-generation fighters are being developed. A new production MIG-29 (probably the MIG-29M), for instance, recently has been stated to be in flight test. This aircraft has an extended empennage (apparently to accommodate defensive avionics and/or the equipment needed for a fly-by-wire flight control system), dog-tooth leading edges on the horizontal stabilators, extended flap trailing edges, and other miscellaneous modifications and upgrades.

Speculation continues over rumors pertaining to the mysterious MIG-33 and MIG-35 designators. As recently as September of 1990, it was acknowledged that ''a new generation combat aircraft equipped with a fiber-optic flight control

Availability of the MIG-29 now has reached the point where its appearance at less prestigious events, such as this showing at a Rockford, Illinois airshow during 1990, is not uncommon.

An Ilyushin Il-76 usually escorts the MIG-29s during their airshow excursions, carrying with it such mandatory items as tow bars and field support and maintenance equipment.

Tow bar for the MIG-29 is robust and long to accommodate the weight and extreme aft position of the nose landing gear. Additionally, it is self-supporting, with crank-down wheels.

During Rockford, Illinois visit, MIG-29 canopies were covered with reflective pad to minimize affect of heat in cockpits. Protective covers also were placed over intakes and exhaust nozzles.

Jay Miller/Aerofax, Inc.

A MIG-29A was demonstrated in flight during the 1988 USAF/USSR exchange visit.

Sustained turn rate capability of the MIG-29A is estimated to be in the 14° to 16° per second range and sustained g capability is estimated to be slightly over 9. Such numbers are affected by payload, however.

system'' was undergoing full-scale testing. Additionally, a new, major redesign of the basic MIG-29 has been announced by MIG. This aircraft is purported to offer a higher maximum speed and ''greatly improved'' landing and takeoff performance. It may later incorporate two-dimensional vectorable exhaust nozzles and is believed to have been given a project number related to its 1988 fiscal year birth.

CONSTRUCTION AND SYSTEMS:

Other designations or related variants include—MIG-29A, MIG-29UB, MIG-29K, MIG-29M,

and ''product 9''. Known airframe numbers: 4401, 4403, 4855, 5116, 5117, 5124, 5125, and 5127.

Production/Prototype Quantities—Approx. 700 aircraft have been manufactured as of this writing including a batch currently under construction in India. As a result of recent politically and economically motivated constraints in the Soviet Union, production of the MIG-29 has slowed considerably and in fact, select related production facilities apparently have been closed.

Cockpit—Both single and two-seat MIG-29s have been built. Both are equipped w/K-36D zero-zero ejection seats. Cockpit arrangement is conventional, w/basically analogue instrumentation and standard stick and rudder pedal controls. Cockpit is elevated with a laminated, stretched

acrylic canopy and single-piece windscreen (probably of glass). Canopy is hinged at the rear and opens vertically via single pneumatic ram in both single- and two-seat versions. Vision is nearly 360° w/some aft restriction. The two-seat aircraft is essentially dimensionally identical to the single-seat but has a long, single-piece, two-transparency canopy. Aft transparency of two-seat aircraft has a periscopic forward viewing unit mounted top and center. The periscope opens and closes automatically via pneumatic rams upon gear extension or retraction. A HUD is mounted above the instrument panel combing (on two-seat aircraft, the HUD is available for the front seat only). There also is a helmet-mounted sighting system available that is integrated with the weapon system. Miscellaneous standard instrumentation includes a horizontal situation indicator (HSI) and DME.

Fuselage—Conventional stressed-skin aluminum alloy construction with composites in select areas. Engines housed in pods suspended from center fuselage structure. Significant blended-body technique is utilized with dielectric panels and fairings placed in several strategic locations, including chine-like root extensions. MIG-29 *Fulcrum C* has deeply curved dorsal hump which presumably houses additional fuel and/or avionics. Fuselage spine ends in drag chute compartment with small dome-shaped covering. At least one new MIG variant (probably the MIG-29M) has an extended dorsal spine similar in physical appearance to that of the Su-27.

Lifting and Control Surfaces—The conventional aluminum construction wings w/approx. 42° leading edge sweepback are equipped w/hydraulically-actuated, segmented leading edge flaps and Fowler-type slotted flaps. Leading edge flaps have two-positions controlled by dedicated computer and driven as a function of Mach number and angle-of-attack. Hydraulically-boosted ailerons are conventional single-piece units. Wing airfoil section is a NASA-type 64A of biconvex section. Thickness/chord ratio at the wing root is 6% and at the tip is 6%. Wing twist is 4.60. Wing chord on centerline is 18 ft. 5 in. (5.6 m.); wing chord at tip is 4 ft. 2 in. (1.27 m.); and wing anhedral is 2°. Wing loading is 84 lb./ft.² (410 kg./m.²). Wings are wet with integral fuel tanks. The hydraulic fluid reservoir is mounted inside these tanks. Six bolts are used to fasten each wing to its respective fuselage attachment points. The navalized MIG-29K is equipped w/hydraulically foldable outer

Anatoly Kvotchur's June 8, 1989 Paris Airshow emrgency egress remains perhaps the most spectacular display yet given, albeit inadvertently, by the exceptional Soviet MIG-29 test pilot.

Configuration of MIG-29A centerline drop tank is considerably different from that of wing drop tanks. Some sources claim the tank is designed for ferry flight use, only.

The rarely-seen-in-the-west "Fulcrum-C". This variant is distinguished by its slightly elevated, or "humped" dorsal spine.

MIG-29UB is a dedicated trainer variant of the standard single-seat aircraft. Though dimensionally virtually identical to its stablemate, it does accommodate a second seat and duplicated basic instrumentation and controls for the instructor pilot in the rear. MIG-29UB, "304", accompanied MIG-29A during the 1990 Rockford, Illinois visit.

MIG-29UB at Rockford, Illinois with protective canopy, intake, and exhaust nozzle covers in place. Though dollyed into position, wing drop tanks have yet to be attached. Noteworthy is tow bar with extended castering wheel assembly. Visible in the background is the MIG contingent's Ilyushin Il-76 support aircraft and a North American B-25J (conversion).

MIG-29K prototype aboard the "Tibilisi" during 1989 trials. Aircraft featured a revised IRST ball, folding outer wing panels, sensor-containing wing tips, a tail hook, and no aux. intake slots.

MIG-29K prototype, as tested aboard the "Tibilisi" had special photo markings. This aircraft almost certainly was an early production MIG-29A modified to the proposed MIG-29K standard.

MIG-29K prototype "trapping" aboard the "Tibilisi". Soviet carrier's arresting cable arrangement is quite similar to that found on western carriers. "Tibilisi" has no discernible catapult system.

wing panels to permit optimum use of carrier deck space. Twin vertical fins, w/a leading edge sweep angle of approx. 40°, are canted outwards 7°, and are each equipped w/single-piece hydraulically-boosted rudders. Vertical fin dorsal extensions on some aircraft house flare dispensing units that now are used throughout the VVS. Late MIG-29As have extended chord rudders. All-moving, slab-type horizontal stabilators w/a leading edge sweep angle of approx. 50° provide both pitch and roll control (the latter being interfaced w/the ailerons). The stabilator airfoil section is a NASA-type 64A004. Thickness/chord ratio at the stabilator root is 4% and at the tip is 4.8%. The vertical tail airfoil section is a NASA-type 64A004. Thickness/chord ratio at the vertical tail root is 4% and at the tip is 4%. The first 100 MIG-29As had extended ventral fins mounted near the horizontal stabilator attachment points. At present, all control surfaces are actuated by the pilot through conventional mechanical linkages and hydraulic boosters. Future MIG-29 variants, however, are expected to be equipped w/advanced fly-by-wire systems. At least one prototype presently is flying w/an FBW system installed. Present manual flight control system has stability augmentation driven by a hybrid analog computer. MIG-29 configuration studies have included canard surfaces on the forward fuselage and a repositioned (forward) wing with associated "relaxed static stability".

Landing Gear—Conventional tricycle arrangement w/single-wheel main gear and steerable dual-wheel nose gear. Mains retract forward into wing roots following a 90° rotational process that is mechanically accommodated. Nose wheels retract aft into well between engine intakes. Retraction rams are hydraulic. All wheels are brake equipped, including nose gear; no anti-skid system; mud/foreign object deflector/guard on nose gear. Main wheel tire size is 30.3 in. by 7.87 in. (770 mm. by 200 mm.) and nose wheel tire size is 20.86 in. by 3.93 in. (530 mm. by 100 mm.). All tire pressures are 180 psi. Wheel track is 10 ft. 2 in. (3.10 m.); wheel base is 12 ft. 0 in. (3.67 m.). The bureau has developed a special machine for boring out the MIG-29's landing gear trunnions. A pneumatically deployed dual canopy drag chute is housed in a container at the far aft end of the empennage section between the vertical tail surfaces. The maximum allowable gear-down speed is 311 mph (500 km/h). Hydraulically-actuated single-piece airbrakes are mounted on the top and bottom of the empennage. A dedicated navalized MIG-29K is to be equipped with a tailhook and in-flight refueling capability.

Miscellaneous Equipment—Coherent RLPK -29 (NATO *Slot Back*) pulse-Doppler radar w/look-down, shoot-down capability. Tracking range of a fighter-size target is 54 mi. (87 km.) in a look-up mode and approx. 31 mi. (50 km.) in a look-down mode. Radar has conventional antenna (not phased-array) and operates in the 54 nanometer range. Known in Soviet service as the "Type 93" it is capable of tracking up to ten targets simultaneously, and can launch a missile every 3 seconds. It is hardened against jamming and has a ground mapping capability. Both single and two-seat MIG-29s are equipped w/an IRST plus LR (infrared search-and-track system collimated w/a laser rangefinder; angular coordinates of a target are fixed by the infrared sensor and distance is determined by a laser pulse unit with a tracking range error of approx. 3 ft. [1 m.]) mounted in a large fairing just ahead of and offset to the right of the windscreen. There also is a helmet-mounted sighting system. Other systems include the SRZO-2 (NATO *Odd Rods*) IFF and *Syrena-3* radar warning equipment. MIG-29UB has the pulse-Doppler radar replaced by a small range-only radar in the nose tip. Additionally on the MIG-29UB,

MIG-29UB touching down following aerobatic display at 1989 Paris Airshow. Noteworthy are open ventral intake slots, though main gear have only barely touched the runway. Also noteworthy is the closed periscopic viewing assembly mounted in the aft cockpit to accommodate the instructor pilot. It appears that activation of this unit is upon pilot command.

The Polish Air Force has received an undisclosed number of MIG-29As and MIG-29UBs during the course of several batch deliveries which began during late 1989. The status of these aircraft (estimated at approx. 40), and the Polish Air Force in general, is unknown as of this writing due to the state of political and economic affairs in the old Eastern bloc countries.

The Czechoslovakian Air Force has accepted a small number of MIG-29As and MIG-29UBs, but as of January 1990, further deliveries have been cancelled. In Czech service, the MIG-29s that have been delivered are expected to supplement extant MIG-21-equipped units. Czech MIG-29s carry a distinctive camouflage scheme unlike that of their VVS counterparts.

John Taylor collection

Full-afterburner takeoff of Czechoslovakian MIG-29A, "9308". The number of MIG-29s currently on Czech Air Force inventory is unknown—but it is considerably less than the normal 40-plus complement.

Piotr Butowski

Czechoslovakian Air Force MIG-29A from the 11th Fighter Regiment at Zatec. Czech "Fulcrums" are virtually identical to their VVS counterparts and are equipped will full-up combat systems.

other miscellaneous combat systems have been deleted or changed. W/both single and two-seat configurations a number of dielectric covers are visible in a variety of positions, though most notably along the leading edge of the wing root chine-like extensions. The aircraft's inertial navigation unit has two alignment modes. Radar altimeter antenna is mounted flush under the nose.

Powerplant/Fuel—Two 18,300 lb. (8,301 kg.) th. (in afterburner) Isotov RD-33 turbofans. Intermediate thrust rating is 11,240 lb. (5,098 kg.). Airflow is 171 lbs./sec. and turbine inlet temp. is 2,500° F. Bypass ratio is 0.65 and pressure ratio is 20. Dry weight of the engine is 2,683 lb. Aircraft thrust-to-weight ratio is 1.1 to 1. Engine controls are hydromechanical (future upgrades include plans for electronic). Engines are dedicated for use in either the left or right engine bay and can not be interchanged. Ramp-type rectangular intakes canted at approx. 9° from the vertical w/ straight-through ducting. Intake leading edge sweep-back angle is approx. 35°. Inlet capture area is 665.60 in.^{2} (.43 m.^{2}) ea., inlet throat area is 561.0 in. $\pm$ (.36 m.^{2}) ea., and exhaust nozzle hingeline area is 1,418.55 in.^{2} (.92 m.^{2}) ea. Internal ramps control mass flow and shock wave formation. Each intake also equipped w/a single-piece, hydraulically-actuated door (hinged at the top forward edge) that completely closes off the intake and forces air to be ingested through a series of five large spring-loaded louver-type auxiliary intakes mounted on the upper surfaces of each wing root extension. System permits operation from rough field environments and prevents FOD occurrence. Doors open automatically at 138 mph (222 km/h) and/or as aircraft weight comes off the landing gear during takeoff. Total internal fuel capacity is 1,153 gal. (4,365 lit.) divided among four fuel tanks as follows: F1 w/2,468.5 lb.; F2 w/1,893.8 lb.; F3 w/2,731.1 lb.; and W1 w/1,705.9 lb.—giving a total of 8,799.3 lb. Three 400 gal. (1,514 lit.) aux. fuel tanks can be carried (one on a centerline pylon, and one under each wing on wing hardpoints). NATO-standard high-pressure fuel receptacle located in left-hand wheel well. Navalized MIG-29K is expected to be equipped with an inflight refueling system of the probe-and-drogue type. Equivalent fuel type is JP-8.

Armament—Normal complement consists of up to six air-to-air missiles including R-23/NATO AA-7 *Apex* (both R-23T w/infrared homing and R-23R w/radar homing); K-13/NATO AA-2 *Atoll*; R-60/NATO AA-8 *Aphid*; NATO AA-10 *Alamo* (both *Alamo B* w/infrared homing and *Alamo C* w/radar homing); R-73/NATO AA-11 *Archer* on six wing

Aerofax, Inc. collection

Czechoslovakian Air Force MIG-29UB, "4401". Semi-gloss camouflage paint utilizes brown and green colors to more closely match Czechoslovakian environmental and terrain considerations. This aircraft is one of only 2 MIG-29UBs thought to have been delivered to the Czechoslovakians.

pylons, one single-barrel 30 mm. GSh-301 cannon w/170 rounds in the left wing root chine extension (weighing 230 lbs. [105 kg.] and capable of a firing rate of 1,500 to 1,800 rounds per minute [each round consisting of a 900 gram bullet and a 400 gram shell]; a muzzle velocity of 2,822 ft./sec. [860 m./sec.]; and a maximum effective range of 3,937 ft. (1,200 m.) to 5,906 ft. (1,800 m.).

Frans Uytenhout

ACRONYMS & ABBREVIATIONS:

AB	air base	km/h	kilometers per hour
BVR	beyond visual range	lb.	pound/pounds
DME	distance measuring	lit.	liter
	equipment	LR	laser rangefinder
FBW	fly by wire	m.	meter/meters
F.S.	Federal Standard	MAI	Moscow Aviation
FLIR	forward looking infrared		Institute
FOD	foreign object damage	MIG	Mikoyan and Gurevich
FSD	full-scale development	mm.	millimeter
ft.	foot/feet	mph	miles per hour
g	gravity	NATO	North Atlantic Treaty
GAZ	state aircraft factory		Organization
HSI	horizontal situation	OKB	experimental design
	indicator		bureau
HUD	heads up display	RAM	Ramenskoye
Il	Ilyushin	sec.	second
in.	inch/inches	TsAGI	Central Aero and
IR	infrared		Hydrodynamics Inst.
IRST	infrared search and	TWS	track-while-scan
	track	VVS	Soviet Air Force

East German Air Force MIG-29A, ''607''. Status of East German ''Fulcrums'' remains undetermined as of this writing. In the interim, however, some aircraft have been flown by western military pilots.

Frans Uytenhout

East German Air Force MIG-29A, ''777'', with white drag chute deployed. Color of drag chute, contrary to some reports, varies considerably. Testing of select expatriated East German Air Force MIG-29s by western pilots have given new insight into this advanced Soviet fighter. It is generally conceded the ''Fulcrum'' is a very competent air combat platform.

Frans Uytenhout

East German Air Force MIG-29UB, ''181'', wearing a grey on grey camouflage pattern more in keeping with that seen on operational VVS aircraft. East German Air Force insigne is readily visible on vertical fin. Noteworthy in this view are extended leading edge flaps and partially retracted nose and main landing gear.

The first prototype MIG-29A survived the flight test program and currently is displayed outdoors at the Soviet Air Force museum at Monino, just outside Moscow. This aircraft differs considerably from its successors in nose configuration, nose landing gear placement, ventral fin inclusion, and other noteworthy details.

MIG-29A, "315", sans centerline external tanks but uploaded with wing drop tanks. Boarding ladder is simply leaning up against the aircraft; normally, the ladder hooks over the cockpit edge and cantilevers out from fuselage side—requiring the pilot to step up about two feet to the first rung.

Czechoslovakian Air Force MIG-29A, "5817", in standard green/green/brown/grey camouflage. Noteworthy is ubiquitous orange tow bar. Visible on upper surface of leading edge extension is maintainance platform which also appears to be a standard fixture around MIG-29 operational units. Leading edge extension is extremely difficult to stand on without it.

East German Air Force MIG-29A, "777", in standard brown/brown/green/green/grey camouflage. As noted elsewhere in this book, the status of ex-East German Air Force MIG-29s is undetermined as of this writing. The new Germany is committed to utilizing western hardware and it is unlikely the "Fulcrums" will find much use in Luftwaffe service.

Two of the air-to-air missiles available for the MIG-29, the AA-11 "Archer" and the AA-10 "Alamo", were statically displayed with the two "Fulcrums" at the 1990 Farnborough Airshow. The "Archers" were equipped with infrared homing heads and the "Alamos" with radar guided heads. All missiles were non-functioning dummies.

SELECTED DRAWINGS

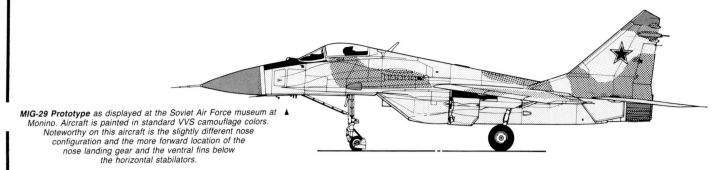

MIG-29 Prototype as displayed at the Soviet Air Force museum at ▲
Monino. Aircraft is painted in standard VVS camouflage colors.
Noteworthy on this aircraft is the slightly different nose
configuration and the more forward location of the
nose landing gear and the ventral fins below
the horizontal stabilators.

MIG-29 *FULCRUM* COLORS AND MARKINGS:

The first MIG-29s to make a public appearance outside the Soviet Union visited Kuopio-Rissala Air Base in Finland during July of 1986 and were painted in a multi-toned gray scheme apparently common to all operational VVS *Fulcrums* with the exception of those in East German and Czechoslovakian service. These aircraft were painted in colors which are close approximations of the following Federal Standard (F.S.) numbers: forward upper fuselage and dorsal spine—darkened gray (F.S. 36375); aft fuselage and vertical stabilizers—gray (F.S. 36375) and gray (F.S. 35237); upper wings—gray (F.S. 36375) and gray (F.S. 35237); lower fuselage—gray (F.S. 36375); anti-glare panel—flat black; all dielectric panels—dark gray (F.S. 36118).

Other operational VVS MIG-29s have been observed in a two-tone scheme that consists of lightened gray (F.S. 35237) and a light to medium green-accented gray (close to F.S. 34233). This scheme's universality and general usage rate is unknown.

The MIG-29A and MIG-29UB as flown and displayed at Paris, Farnborough, Singapore, and other airshows around the globe were painted in a two-tone gray and gray/green scheme as follows: upper fuselage, wings, and vertical stabilizers—gray (F.S. 36628) and gray/green (F.S. 34233); lower surfaces—gray (F.S. 36628); anti-glare panel—flat black; and dielectric panels—dark gray (F.S. 36118).

East German MIG-29 colors approximate those used by AF aircraft utilized in the Southeast Asia conflict; upper fuselage, wings, and vertical stabilizers—tan (F.S. 36415), brown (F.S. 30045), light green (F.S. 34410), and dark green (F.S. 34092); lower surfaces—gray (F.S. 36375); anti-glare panel—flat black; radome and dielectric panels—dark gray (F.S. 36118).

In all cases, the landing gear and wheel wells appear to be light gray (F.S. 36375), the cockpit tub appears to be gray (F.S. 36375); the instrument bezels are flat black; and the wheel hubs are green (F.S. 34226).

Czechoslovakian MIG-29 colors duplicate the old East German scheme. However, Czech aircraft do not have the brown (F.S. 30045) on the upper surface.

PERFORMANCE AND SPECIFICATIONS:

Length—56 ft. 10 in. (17.32 m.)
Wingspan—36 ft. 5 in. (11.36 m.)
Wing area—410.07 ft.² (38.1 m.²)
Wing aspect ratio—3.430
Wing lead. edge sweep angle—41.41°
Wing trail. edge sweep angle—11.46°
Wing taper ratio—0.2633
Wing root chord—208.42 in. (5.29 m.)
Wing tip chord—54.87 in. (1.39 m.)
Wing mean aero. chord—146.34 in. (3.71 m.)
Wing incidence—2.90
Wing dihedral—minus 2.70
Horiz. tail area—76.95 ft.² (7.14 m.²)
Horiz. tail aspect ratio—2.374
Horiz. tail span (ea.)—6 ft. 7 in. (2 m.)
Horiz. tail lead. edge sweep angle—52°
Horiz. tail trail. edge sweep angle—24.7°
Horiz. tail taper ratio—0.3405
Horiz. tail root chord—101.93 in. (2.59 m.)
Horiz. tail tip chord—34.71 in. (.88 m.)
Horiz. tail mean aero. chord—73.83 in. (1.88 m.)
Horiz. tail incidence—2.90
Horiz. tail dihedral—minus 7.25°
Height—15 ft. 6 in. (4.73 m.)
Vert. tail area—144.44 ft.²
Vert. tail aspect ratio—2.440
Vert. tail height—9.38 ft. (2.85 m.)
Vert. tail lead. edge sweep angle—51.10°
Vert. tail taper ratio—0.1974
Vert. tail trail. edge sweep angle—8°
Vert. tail root chord—154.25 in. (3.92 m.)
Vert. tail tip chord—30.45 in. (.77 m.)
Vert. tail mean aero. chord—106.18 in. (2.70 m.)
Empty weight—18,025 lb. (8,175 kg.)
Gross weight—39,683 lb. (18,000 kg.)
Avg. combat th. to weight—1.1
Instantaneous turn capability—20° to 22°/sec.
Sustained turn capability—14° to 16°/sec.
Max. speed @ s.l.—805 mph (1,300 km/h)
Max. speed—1,541 mph (2,480 km/h) @ 30,000 ft. (20,260 m.)
Service ceiling—54,542 ft. (17,000 m.)
Max. range—1,301 mi. (2,094 km.)
Notes—Max. sustained g. is 9. Takeoff speed is 162 mph to 174 mph (260 km/h to 280 km/h); landing speed is 143 mph (230 km/h). Takeoff run is 770 ft. (240 m.); and landing run is 1,925 ft. (600 m.).

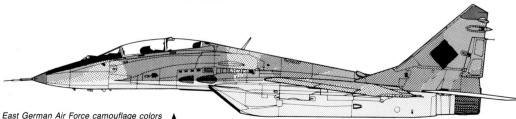

▲ **Iraqi Air Force MIG-29A** during the first weeks of **Operation Desert Storm**. During this period, US and allied air forces aircraft were credited with downing between six and eleven Iraqi MIG-29s. Presumably, others escaped combat by fleeing to Iran. Iraqi Air Force aircraft are painted in the standard VVS camouflage colors.

MIG-29 "Fulcrum C" bearing typical VVS camouflage colors. This variant is ▲
nicknamed Fatback with increased internal fuel and upgraded avionics.

MIG-29UB bearing old East German Air Force camouflage colors ▲
consisting of a brown/tan/green scheme completely different
from the two-tone gray colors of the VVS, Czechoslovakian,
Hungarian, Indian, and other air forces.

MIG-29 *Fulcrum*, "Blue 06"

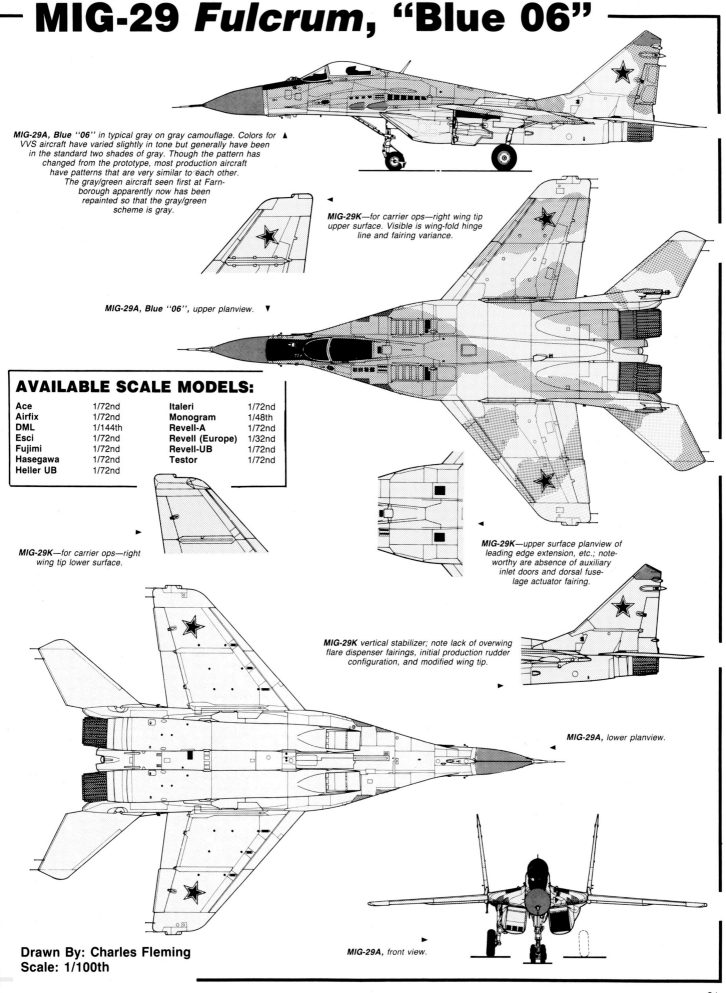

MIG-29A, Blue "06" in typical gray on gray camouflage. Colors for VVS aircraft have varied slightly in tone but generally have been in the standard two shades of gray. Though the pattern has changed from the prototype, most production aircraft have patterns that are very similar to each other. The gray/green aircraft seen first at Farnborough apparently now has been repainted so that the gray/green scheme is gray.

MIG-29K—for carrier ops—right wing tip upper surface. Visible is wing-fold hinge line and fairing variance.

MIG-29A, Blue "06", upper planview. ▼

AVAILABLE SCALE MODELS:

Ace	1/72nd	Italeri	1/72nd
Airfix	1/72nd	Monogram	1/48th
DML	1/144th	Revell-A	1/72nd
Esci	1/72nd	Revell (Europe)	1/32nd
Fujimi	1/72nd	Revell-UB	1/72nd
Hasegawa	1/72nd	Testor	1/72nd
Heller UB	1/72nd		

MIG-29K—for carrier ops—right wing tip lower surface.

MIG-29K—upper surface planview of leading edge extension, etc.; noteworthy are absence of auxiliary inlet doors and dorsal fuselage actuator fairing.

MIG-29K vertical stabilizer; note lack of overwing flare dispenser fairings, initial production rudder configuration, and modified wing tip.

MIG-29A, lower planview. ◄

Drawn By: Charles Fleming
Scale: 1/100th

MIG-29A, front view. ►

Achille Vigna

A Yugoslavian MIG-29A, "18112", at Brnik AB on September 24, 1989. Camouflage appears to be exactly like that used on VVS aircraft. Visible to right is centerline drop tank. In Yugoslavia, the MIG-29 is designated L-18 (L = Lovac which means "fighter"). The first "Fulcrus" were delivered to Yugoslavia during October of 1987.

Frans Uytenhout

East German Air Force MIG-29UM, "179", at start of taxi. Noteworthy is extended aft-seat periscope for instructor pilot forward view, folded instrument training hood (front seat), and open dorsal auxiliary intake slots. Light coloring to camouflage is reminiscent of VVS markings, but is more pastel in appearance.

Main instrument panel of standard production MIG-29A in VVS service. Compare this panel with that of MIG-29A utilized for airshow and display work (see page 25).

MIG-29UB, "304", instrument panel is equipped with standard HUD and other operational systems. Changes for airshow circuit are few.

Aft instrument panel of MIG-29UB, "304". As no other aft-seat view is available, it is unknown how different this aircraft is from operational "UBs".

Headrest and drogue-arm cylinder assemblies of the MIG-29A's K-36DM series 2 ejection seat. Circuit breaker box is visible to the rear.

Some 40 MIG-29As and MIG-29UBs presently are on the operational Iraqi Air Force inventory. These aircraft are considered a major threat to opposition forces operating in the Middle Eastern Theatre.

The Indian Air Force has accepted initial MIG-29A and MIG-29UB deliveries and has confirmed plans to have the type produced indigenously by Hindustan Aircraft Industries.

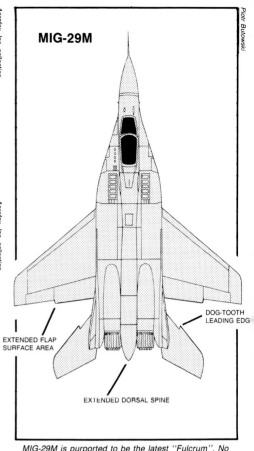

MIG-29M

DOG-TOOTH
LEADING EDG

EXTENDED FLAP
SURFACE AREA

EXTENDED DORSAL SPINE

MIG-29M is purported to be the latest "Fulcrum". No photos have been released as of this writing.

Two Soviet-supplied Indian Air Force MIG-29As, K8706 (foreground) and K8714, depart an unidentified Indian Air Force base at the beginning of a training mission.

The MIG-29 is referred to as the L-18 in Yugoslavian Air Force service. The first "Fulcrums" delivered to Yugoslavia arrived during October of 1987.

Yugoslovian Air Force MIG-29UB, "302", during final approach to landing at an unidentified Yugoslavian air base. Noteworthy is the barely discernible extended periscopic viewing assembly for the instructor pilot located in the rear seat. Also noteworthy is the fact that the MIG-29UB, like the MIG-29A, is capable of accommodating six missile rails.

IN DETAIL

MIG-29A instrument panel is almost totally analogue with few digitized presentations. This particular panel has been modified for western demonstration program.

MIG-29A left console area includes unusual tube-mounted linear throttle assembly and associated systems switches. Control stick is visible to right.

MIG-29A right console area includes environmental system controls, warning panel push-switches, and some weapons system controls. To far left is radar warning panel.

MIG-29UB front instrument panel supports conventional HUD assembly. Instrumentation and radar CRT to right are virtually identical to that of MIG-29A.

MIG-29UB front seat left console echoes panel layouts and throttle quandrant design found on single-seat aircraft. Noteworthy are oxygen and com. connections.

MIG-29UB front seat right console echoes panel layouts found on single-seat aircraft. Warning panel push-switch quantity, however, is fewer in number.

Jay Miller/Aerofax, Inc.

MIG-29UB back seat left console is a minimalized facsimile of the arrangement found in the front seat and also in the single-seat aircraft.

Jay Miller/Aerofax, Inc.

MIG-29UB back seat instrument panel is equipped with essential instrumentation and auxiliary radar CRT-type display offset to right.

MIG-29UB back seat right console is a minimalized facsimile of the arrangement found in the front seat and also in the single-seat aircraft.

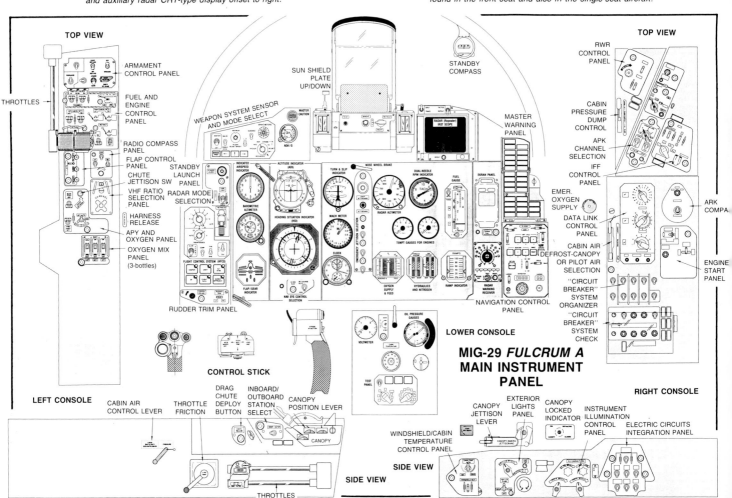

TOP VIEW

- ARMAMENT CONTROL PANEL
- FUEL AND ENGINE CONTROL PANEL
- RADIO COMPASS PANEL
- FLAP CONTROL PANEL
- CHUTE JETTISON SW
- VHF RATIO SELECTION PANEL
- HARNESS RELEASE
- APY AND OXYGEN PANEL
- OXYGEN MIX PANEL (3-bottles)

THROTTLES

STANDBY LAUNCH PANEL

RADAR MODE SELECTION

WEAPON SYSTEM SENSOR AND MODE SELECT

SUN SHIELD PLATE UP/DOWN

STANDBY COMPASS

MASTER CAUTION

ADA/G

RADAR (Repeater) IRST SCOPE

MASTER WARNING PANEL

INDICATED AIRSPEED INDICATOR

ALTITUDE INDICATOR (ADI)

TURN & SLIP INDICATOR

NOSE WHEEL BRAKE

DUAL-NEEDLE RPM INDICATOR

FUEL GAUGE

EKRAN PANEL

BAROMETRIC ALTIMETER

HEADING SITUATION INDICATOR (HSI)

MACH METER

RADAR ALTIMETER

EMER. OXYGEN SUPPLY

CLOCK

TEMPT GAUGES FOR ENGINES

FLIGHT CONTROL SYSTEM (AFCS)

OXYGEN SUPPLY & FEED

HYDRAULICS AND NITROGEN

RAMP INDICATOR

RADAR WARNING RECEIVER

NAVIGATION CONTROL PANEL

FLAP/GEAR INDICATOR

NAV SYS CONTROL SELECTION

RUDDER TRIM PANEL

OIL PRESSURE GAUGES

VOLTMETER

TEST PANEL

LOWER CONSOLE

CONTROL STICK

DRAG CHUTE DEPLOY BUTTON

INBOARD/OUTBOARD STATION SELECT

CANOPY POSITION LEVER

CANOPY

LEFT CONSOLE

CABIN AIR CONTROL LEVER

THROTTLE FRICTION

THROTTLES

SIDE VIEW

MIG-29 *FULCRUM A* MAIN INSTRUMENT PANEL

TOP VIEW

- RWR CONTROL PANEL
- CABIN PRESSURE DUMP CONTROL
- APK CHANNEL SELECTION
- IFF CONTROL PANEL
- ARK COMPA
- DATA LINK CONTROL PANEL
- CABIN AIR DEFROST-CANOPY OR PILOT AIR SELECTION
- "CIRCUIT BREAKER" SYSTEM ORGANIZER
- "CIRCUIT BREAKER" SYSTEM CHECK

ENGINE START PANEL

RIGHT CONSOLE

CANOPY JETTISON LEVER

EXTERIOR LIGHTS PANEL

CANOPY LOCKED INDICATOR

INSTRUMENT ILLUMINATION CONTROL PANEL

ELECTRIC CIRCUITS INTEGRATION PANEL

WINDSHIELD/CABIN TEMPERATURE CONTROL PANEL

SIDE VIEW

Headrest and drogue-arm cylinder assemblies of the MIG-29A's K-36DM ejection seat.

Circuit breaker box and associated reset buttons, seemingly inaccessible to pilot, is mounted immediately aft of the K-36DM ejection seat headrest in the MIG-29A.

Rear K-36DM ejection seat of MIG-29UB. Visible behind it is hydraulic actuator for canopy.

MIG-29UB canopy is two-piece assembly. Aft transparency is equipped with built-in periscopic assembly to accommodate instructor pilot viewing requirements. Note folded instrument training hood aft of front pilot.

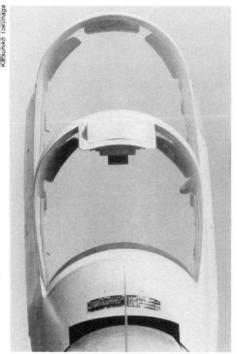

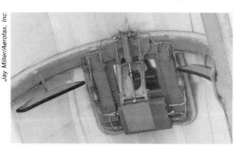

MIG-29UB's (retracted) periscope assembly appears to be pneumatically actuated.

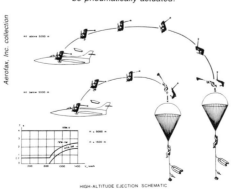

HIGH-ALTITUDE EJECTION SCHEMATIC

MIG-29UB's (retracted) periscope assembly is mounted on center in aft transparency.

Zero-zero K-36D ejection seat provides safe emergency egress throughout the MIG-29's flight envelope.

The K-36DM ejection seat, found in several Soviet combat aircraft, is rocket-propelled.

The MIG-29A's single-piece nose radome is constructed of conventional composite-type dielectric materials and is removeable for radar system access.

Other than a primary, circular supporting structure and sensor lines associated with the pitot assembly, the nose radome is made totally of dielectric materials.

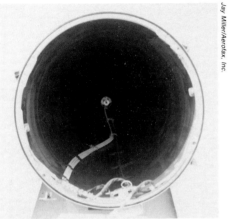

Pitot sensor lines are routed aft at the bottom of the radome. Quick disconnects permit rapid removal.

Yaw vane, radar altimeter dielectric panel, and ILS antennas are mounted in ventral nose fairing.

Inclusive of rapid and easy removal of the dielectric nose radome, a variety of access panels are easily opened to provide access to the radar and miscellaneous avionics and sub-systems.

Radar altimeter fairing is easily-discerned circular dielectric panel on ventral nose fairing.

A pitot sensor is mounted to the right of the articulated infrared search and track/laser rangefinder ball and associated fairing. Half-cone shaped device ahead of IRST/LR may be removable.

Several pitot-type sensors are visible at various positions on the MIG-29A. Data is networked to computers for weapon system and flight instruments.

What appears to be an electric heating element is imbedded in the "Fulcrum's" windscreen. AoA vane is visible lower left.

A single yaw and two pitch AoA vanes are mounted underneath and on each side of the nose, aft of the radome. ILS antennas also are mounted top and bottom.

The MIG-29UB is equipped only with a small range-finding radar but does retain the IRST/LR ball and associated assembly ahead of the windscreen.

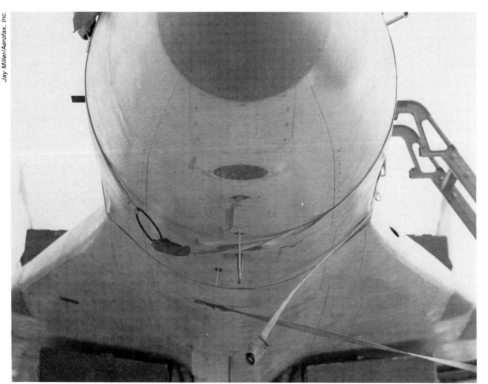

MIG-29UB does not retain the special fairing for the radar altimeter and associated systems, but it does retain the rardar altimeter and its associated round dielectric panels.

Automated testing systems are accessed by opening several different non-structural panels.

It is presumed that avionics upgrades found in the "Fulcrum C" are located in its humped dorsal spine.

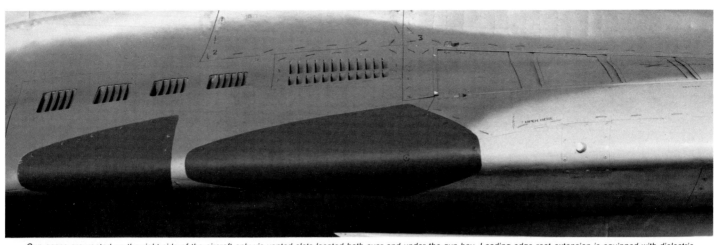

Gun gases are vented on the right side of the aircraft only via vented slots located both over and under the gun bay. Leading edge root extension is equipped with dielectric fairings accommodating radar homing and warning antenna and related systems. Noteworthy in this view are visible hand-applied alignment marks for panel fasteners.

MIG-29A left side auxiliary intake slots with spring-loaded doors in closed position.

MIG-29A right side auxiliary intake slots with spring-loaded doors in closed position.

MIG-29A tunnel area between engine nacelles, looking aft. Fuel tank connection points are visible.

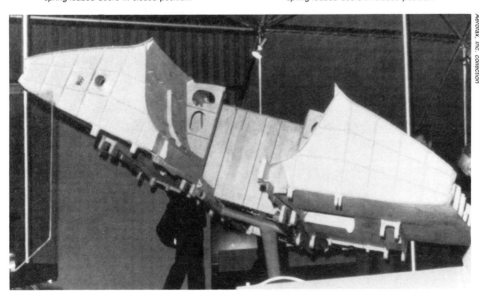

MIG-29 central carry-through structure is thought to be of titanium alloy. Most of the major dynamic loads imparted on the aircraft, including engine weight and wing lift, are born by this complex welded-up assembly.

Looking forward from aft of the right-side vertical tail/engine area empennage interface.

A small, hydraulically-actuated, split surface airbrake is mounted between the engine exhaust nozzles and around the drag chute housing canister.

A small, half-dome shaped cap, hinged at the bottom, covers the drag chute housing canister and pops open upon pilot command following landing.

Left side flap, looking aft. The single-piece, hydraulically actuated, mixed materials construction flaps function upon pilot command and are used primarily in the low-speed segment of the performance envelope.

Though the hydraulically actuated ailerons are similar to the flaps in terms of materials and construction, they are considerably smaller in terms of surface area.

The leading edge flaps are automatically scheduled to function as a result of airspeed, g, and AoA.

The wingtip radar warning antennas and night flying lights are mounted in a rather crude, non-aerodynamically refined fairing. The navalized MIG-29K has a considerably different fairing.

31

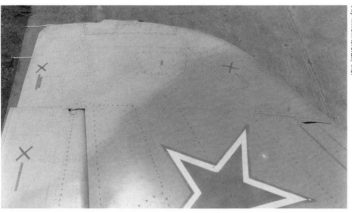

Jay Miller/Aerofax, Inc.

Katsuhiko Tokunaga

Rounded wingtip is of primarily aluminum materials and is equipped with rigid static discharge devices and several removable interior access panels.

MIG-29A single-piece slab-type stabilator of primarily aluminum construction is hydraulically actuated and equipped with rigid static discharge devices.

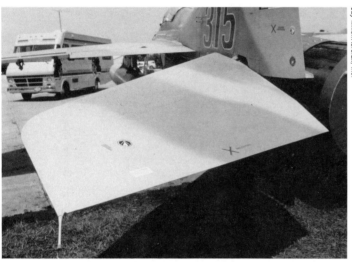

Jay Miller/Aerofax, Inc.

Jay Miller/Aerofax, Inc.

MIG-29A recently has been seen with single static discharge device, rather than two. Stabilators works both differentially and in unison.

Stabilator is attached to empennage via single load bearing arm assembly in aerodynamic fairing. Stabilator stub-section is rigidly attached to empennage.

Jay Miller/Aerofax, Inc.

Jay Miller/Aerofax, Inc.

MIG-29A left vertical tail inside view. Rudder is hydraullically actuated. Upper trailing edge is equipped with bullet fairings for sensors and antenna.

MIG-29A right vertical tail inside view. Rudder is single-piece unit of aluminum and composite construction. Noteworthy is exposed actuator arm.

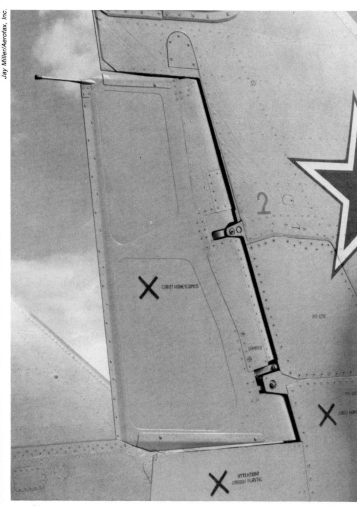

Dielectric panel covers com. antennas at left vertical fin tip. Nav. light and warning and nav. antenna fairings are mounted on trailing edge.

Single piece aluminum and composite construction hydraulically actuated rudder is equipped with rigid static discharge device.

Dielectric panel covers com. antennas at right vertical fin tip. On trailing edge are radar warning and navigation sytem antennas (top).

Steerable nose landing gear is equipped with independent disc-type braking unit and dedicated mud guard.

Nose landing gear is rugged and optimized for rough field operations. Unit retracts aft with the assistance of a single hydraulic actuating ram. Twin-wheel unit automatically self-aligns during retraction process.

Jay Miller/Aerofax, Inc.

Fully-extended nose gear strut and attachment mechanism for dedicated tow bar. Noteworthy are gear anti-sway struts.

Jay Miller/Aerofax, Inc.

Anti-torque scissor is mounted forward of strut assembly. Small strut mounted aft supports mud guard.

DoD via Dick Cole

Rear view of nose landing gear details mud guard and associated mounting system.

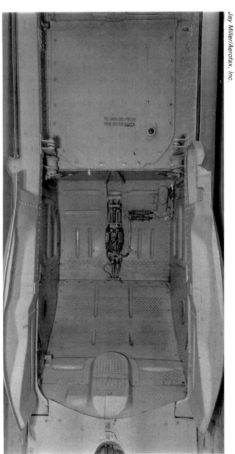

Jay Miller/Aerofax, Inc.

Nose landing gear well is tightly toleranced, but generally uncluttered.

Jay Miller/Aerofax, Inc.

Nose landing gear strut attaches to fuselage structure through Y-shaped yoke assembly.

Main gear well primary doors serve as mounting points for taxi/landing lights. Strut clearance impressions appear extremely crude and hand-formed.

Main landing gear retracts forward under power supplied by a single, rear-mounted hydraulic ram. Tires are optimized for rough field operation.

Main gear well primary doors have single hinge at each end and are hydro-mechanically closed in sequence with the landing gear.

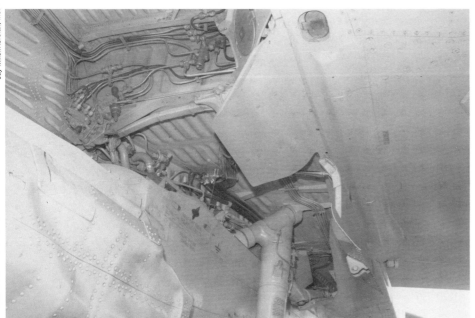

Main gear well door is opened and closed via single hydraulic ram and hinged arm assembly.

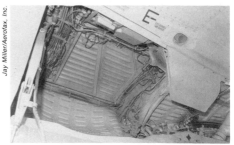

Because of retraction geometry, main gear well is relatively shallow. Visible are various high-pressure hydraulic and pneumatic lines, miscellaneous fuel plumbing lines, and angled strut hinge attachment point.

High-pressure hydraulic systems permit the use of small diameter tubing in areas such as gear wells.

Rigidly mounted landing/taxi lights normally switch on as main landing gear extend.

The cruciform-shaped primary drag chute canopy is physically pulled from the drag chute canister by a spring-ejected drogue chute. The latter is released as the dome-shaped canister cover opens.

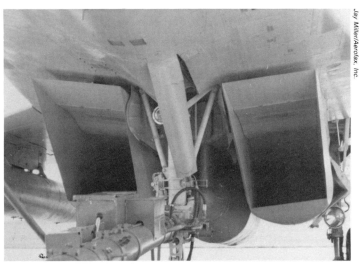

Variable-ramp area intakes are governed by computer input resulting from numerous externally-sensed variables such as airspeed, altitude, and AoA.

Once engine start-up cycle is initiated, FOD doors in intakes move down into position and ventral auxiliary intakes open. Cycle is automatic unless overridden.

Ventrally positioned auxiliary intakes remain functional throughout "Fulcrum's" flight envelope, though they are in full-open position almost constantly while aircraft taxis or operates on the ground. During maneuvering flight, the auxiliary intake spring loaded doors can be seen constantly opening and clsoing at a high rate of speed.

The Isotov RD-33 engines have been stated by authoritative sources to be turbofans, but to date, there remains some debate as to whether this is so.

Isotov RD-33's unusual exhaust nozzle design appears to provide some validity to the turbofan claim, but exactly how it functions remains undisclosed.

MIG-29's centerline drop tank fits so tightly in space between the engine nacelles that anti-sway snubbers are required on either side of its aft end. Noteworthy in this view also are the afterburner spray bar assemblies, the half-dome cover for the drag chute canister, and the hinge arms for the lower half of the split airbrake.

The MIG-29 can carry two external wing tanks, each with a capacity of 400 gallons. The centerline tank, though appearing more capacious, also has a capacity of 400 gallons. All three tanks are presumed to be jettisonable upon pilot command. Special dollies are utilized to move tanks on ground but apparently have limited vertical height capability.

Two large load bearing pins with threaded ends secure the drop tanks to the wings. The pins are shoved through mounting holes and bolted into position.

Each nose cap is equipped with a small canard surface to provide a downward pitching moment to the tank during the ejection process.

The centerline tank is a relatively crude design optimized strictly for long-range ferry missions. It apparently can not be utilized in supersonic flight.

An exhaust port is cut through the aft end of the tank to accommodate the needs of what apparently is an internally-mounted auxiliary power unit.

Cooling vent holes are visible in aft end of centerline tank. Tank attachment lugs are visible at 11 and 1 o'clock positions aft of anti-sway snubbers.

Single-point refueling can be accomplished using a NATO-standard connector mounted behind a small door located in the left main gear well.

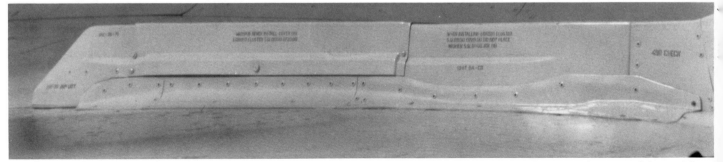

Combination chaff/flare dispensers are mounted integral with the vertical fin root extensions visible above the wing roots. Addition of the fin root extensions apparently improved directional stability to the point that ventral fins seen on early production MIG-29s could be removed. The dispensers themselves are removable and are technically field replaceable.

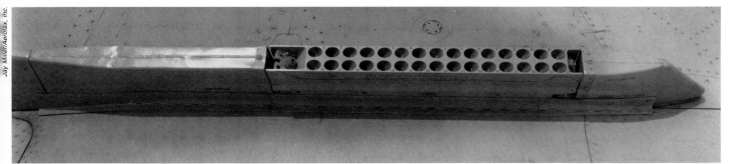

The combination chaff/flare dispenser ejector holes are angled inward slightly toward the aircraft centerline and aimed forward. Thirty packages of chaff or thirty flares (or combinations of both) can be ejected as necessary from each unit. Ejected chaff apparently progresses aft between the vertical tail surfaces before spreading.

Two outboard wing pylons are optimized for weapons carriage such as AA-8 air-to-air missile. Inboard pylons can be used for either missiles or drop tanks.

Missile rail design generally emulates that of western configurations, but pylon attachment to rail and wing is considerably less sophisticated.

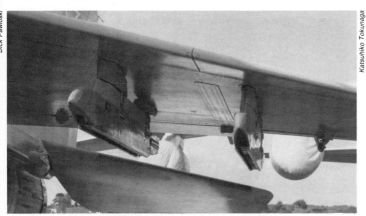

MIG-29 can be flown only with outboard wing pylons in place. Caps are used to cover holes left when pylons are not carried.

R-73, known in the west under the NATO-assigned designator AA-11 "Archer", was formally unveiled to the west during the 1990 Farnborough Airshow.

The R-73 is infrared guided and equipped with a vectorable exhaust nozzle to complement its extensive collection of aerodynamic surfaces.

R-73 exhaust nozzle vectoring is accommodate through impinging surfaces which move in and out of exhaust gas flow.

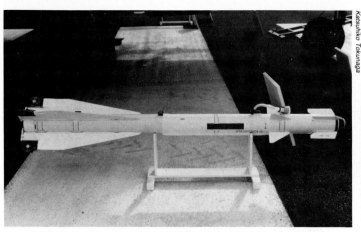

R-60, known in the west under the NATO-assigned designator AA-8 ''Aphid'', can be equipped either with infrared (shown) or radar guidance systems.

The NATO designated AA-10 ''Alamo'' is one of the most formidable of Soviet air-to-air weapons and is deployed in at least three different burn lengths.

During the 1990 Farnborough Airshow, MIG-29A, ''315'', was demonstrated statically and flown equipped with what apparently were two dummy AA-10 ''Alamos'' (inboard two pylons) and four dummy AA-11 ''Archers''. The ''Fulcrum's'' ability to perform extraordinary maneuvers with these weapons in place proved of great interest to western military observers.